Celestine

and the Penguins

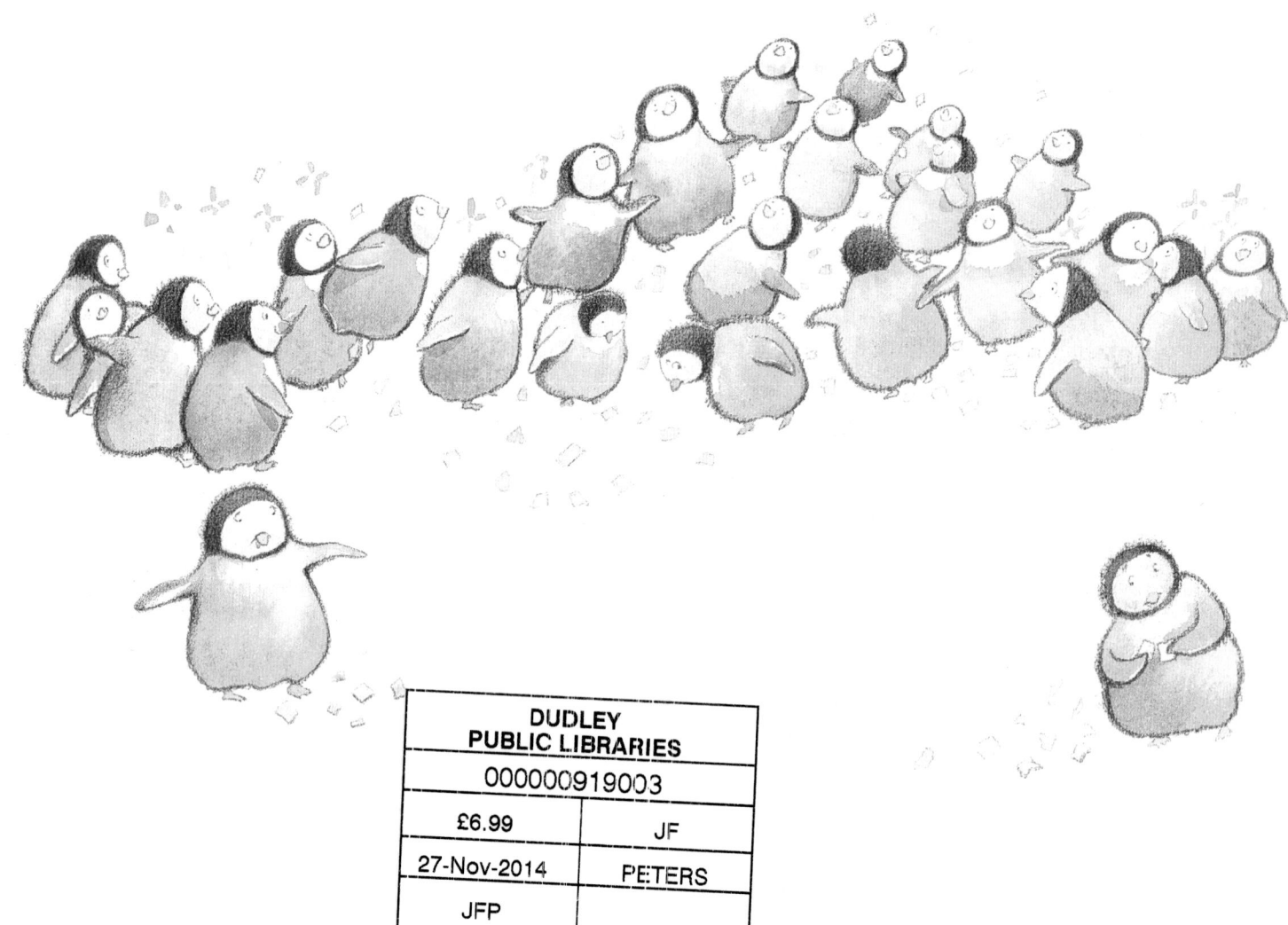

Celestine

and the Penguins

Celestine was all ready for winter.

But the garden was still bright with a few late flowers and yellow leaves waved lazily from the trees.

"Why won't you snow?" she shouted crossly at the sky.

"It's supposed to be cold!"

The next day was just as warm
when Celestine went out to play.

She did her best to
pretend it had snowed,
but…

"Mud-ducks and mud-balls are
horrible and brown," she decided.

"I'll have to make
some lovely white
snow myself!"

"Ta-da!" cried Celestine, throwing cotton wool balls into the air.

But each one just fell straight to the ground.

"Oh dear," she sighed. "Cotton wool is too lumpy. What else can I try?"

"Hooray!" sang Celestine,
throwing handfuls of flour into the air.

But that just made her cough!

"I know," she smiled, "little pieces of paper
will be just right!"

"Yippee!"

she shouted.

"It's snowing!"

Just then, Celestine caught
sight of something out of the
corner of her eye.

She stopped — and ve-ery
slowly, turned around…

Behind her, the garden was bobbing with lots and lots and LOTS of baby penguins, all milling about.

"Snow!"

"SNOW!"

"SNOW!"

"Snow!"

"Snow!"

"It's snowing!"

"Snow!"

"SNOW!"

"Snow!"

"Oh my goodness!"
squeaked Celestine. "Where did
you all come from?"

"We're lost," said one little penguin.
"A long way from home," sighed another.
"Can we stay with you?" asked a third.

"But h-h-how did you get here?" asked Celestine.

One little penguin began to explain.
"We come from a cold place, far away. We were
huddled, fast-asleep, in our nursery," he began.

"Our mums and dads had gone fishing
for dinner when a storm began.

The wind blew,
the sea roared
and then –
crack!

The ice split in two...
we were adrift!"

"We were carried on the waves, further and further from home. Up and down, UP and DOWN,

UP and

DOWN."

"We called
and called...

as the sea got
warmer and
warmer...

and our iceberg
got smaller
and

smaller...

But, just in time, we
landed on a little beach!

Straight away we set off to look for snow.

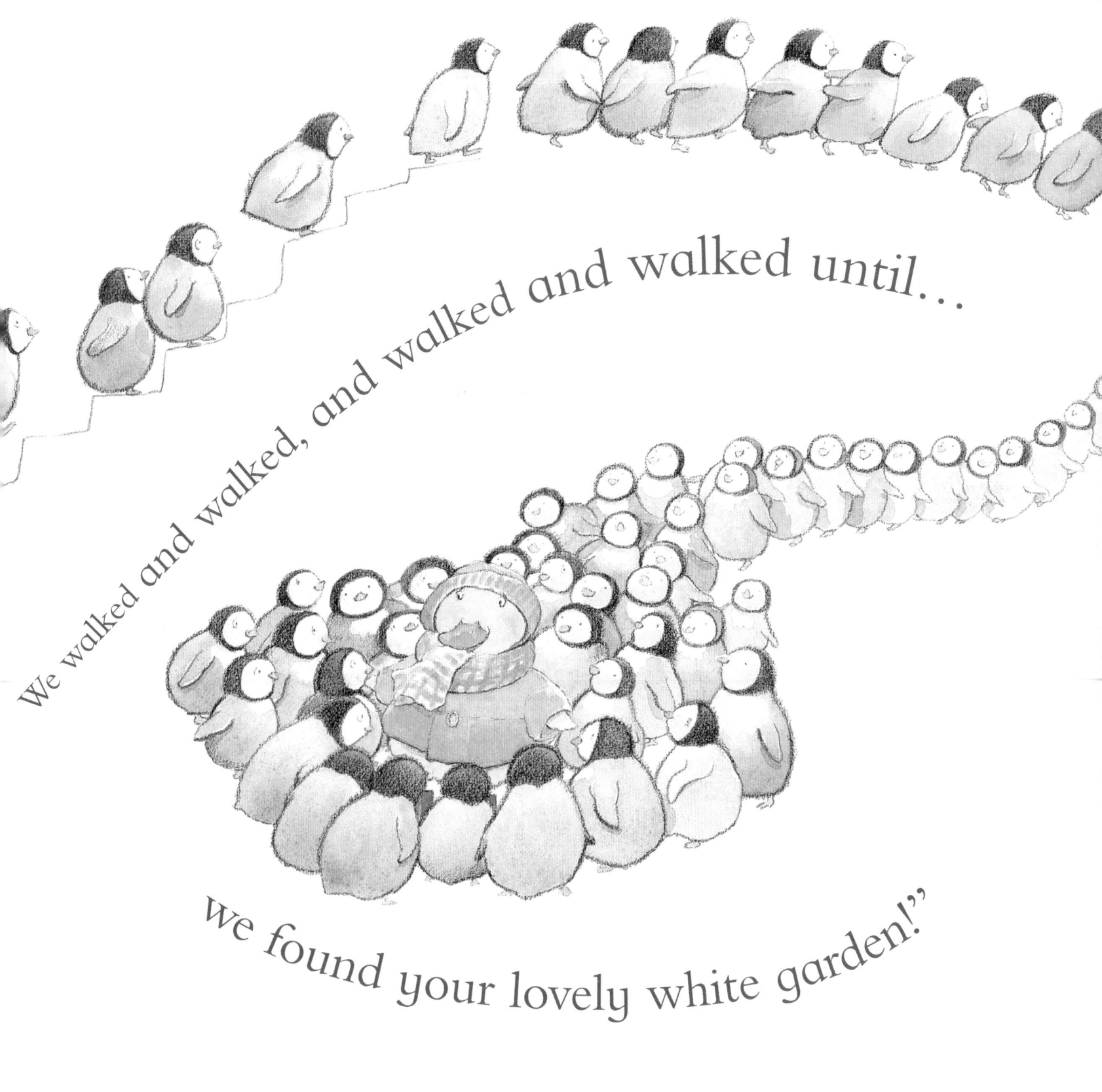

We walked and walked, and walked and walked and walked until...

we found your lovely white garden!"

"But this isn't **real** snow!"
said one of the baby penguins, sadly.

"It's not **cold** and **crunchy**
or **sparkly** and **slidey!**"

"And now we are too hot and…
we want to go hooome!"
wailed the littlest penguins.

"I'm very sorry," sighed Celestine, looking at the pieces of paper. "I did my best."

She sat down and thought for a moment.

"I know what to do," she said happily. "I've got a **brilliant** idea – come with me!"

"This is called a FREEZER," announced Celestine. "It's very cold in here – you'll like it. Careful please, no pushing - there's room for everyone if I take all these things out."

But there wasn't… quite…

"Hmm," thought Celestine.

Then she had another **excellent** idea…

Celestine took loads of lollies from the freezer and found some elastic bands in a kitchen drawer.

"Come on!" she cried.

"With these slippery lollies on our feet we can go

ice lolly skating!"

"And how about making a
pea-and-ice
SLIDE!

But when Celestine looked down at the floor – what a mess!
It had begun to look like green soup!
"Um," thought Celestine. "Let's play upstairs instead!
Follow me to the bathroom…

I've just had my **best idea** yet!"

"More peas and ice!"

"More peas and ice!"

"Let's make ice-cream-bergs!" said Celestine.
"But this time try not to make so much mess!"

Celestine and the penguins were having
a lovely, sticky, splashy time, when
someone knocked at the door…

Knock!

Knock!

"Who's there?"
asked Celestine.

"It's **Mummy**," came the reply.

Then Mummy opened the door…

"Celestine!
What are you doing?"

she shrieked.

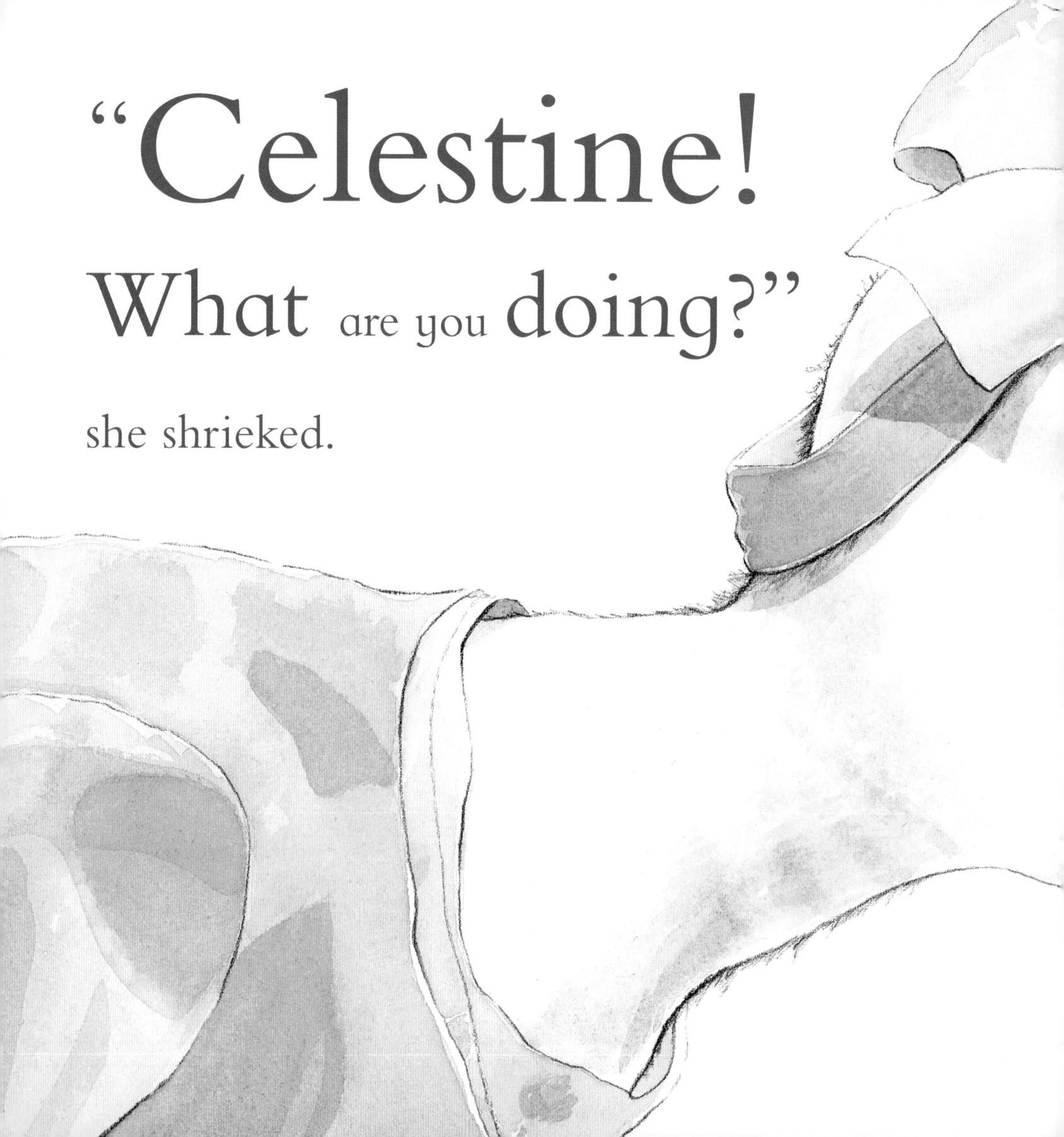

"I TOLD you!" explained Celestine.
"I was playing with the baby penguins.
And Mum – they've been EVER so
naughty!"

Celestine tried to
explain everything.

"I see," said Mrs Duck, when
Celestine had finished.
"Their parents must be very
worried. These little penguins need
to go home straight away!"

Mrs Duck and Celestine
squeezed all the little
penguins onto the bus
and together they
set off towards
the sea.

Down at the harbour, an explorer's ship
was getting ready to set sail.
"Don't worry, Mrs Duck,"
the captain promised,
"I'll see all these baby
penguins safely
back home."

"Thank you, Celestine," called the penguins as they jumped on board, waving goodbye with their tickets.

"Goodbye! Goodbye!" called Celestine.

As the ship chugged off towards the horizon, Celestine felt
something soft and cold tickle her cheek.

She looked up at the sky.

It was snowing!
"Hooray!" she danced.
"Tomorrow I can play in the snow all day!"

"Of course you can!" smiled Mum...

"After you've helped me
clean up all that mess!"

For Nina and Aaron – P.I.

A TEMPLAR BOOK

First published in the UK in 2008 by Templar Publishing.
This softback edition published in 2014 by Templar Publishing,
an imprint of The Templar Company Limited,
Deepdene Lodge, Deepdene Avenue, Dorking, Surrey, RH5 4AT, UK
www.templarco.co.uk

1 3 5 7 9 10 8 6 4 2

ISBN 978-1-78370-118-6

Designed by Caroline Reeves
Edited by Stella Gurney

Printed in China

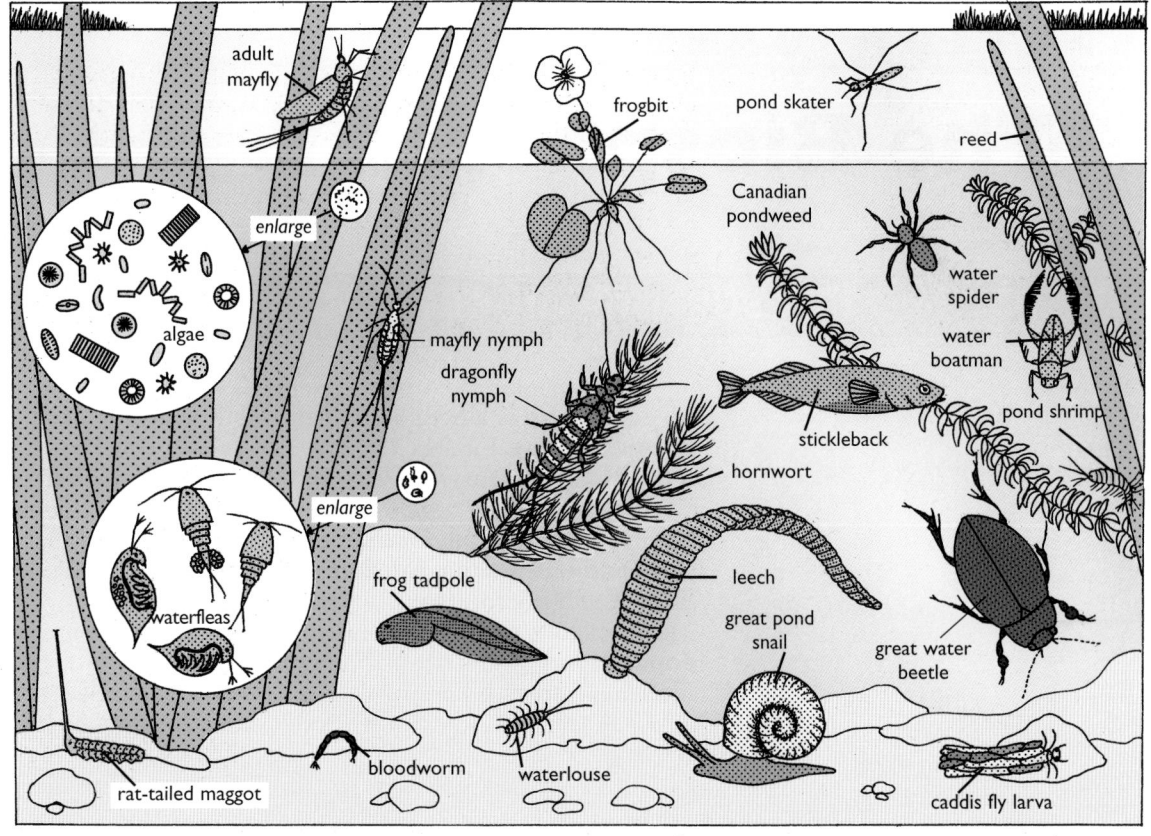

Figure 1.3 Fresh water ecosystem

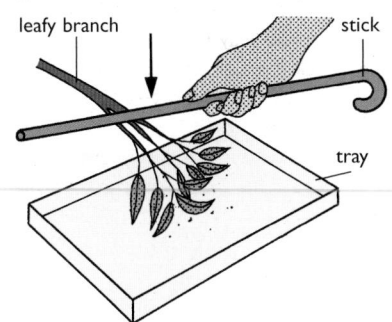

Figure 1.5 Tree beating

Figure 1.4 Rockpool ecosystem

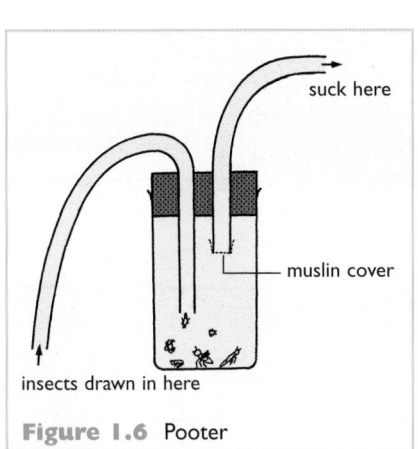

Figure 1.6 Pooter

Practical investigation of an ecosystem

The study of an ecosystem involves:
- finding out which plants and animals live there;
- finding out how abundant (rare, common, etc.) these organisms are;
- investigating the reasons why the organisms live there.

The Biosphere

CHAPTER ONE

Investigating an ecosystem

An **ecosystem** is a natural biological unit which is made up of living and non-living parts. Figures 1.1, 1.2, 1.3 and 1.4 show some examples of ecosystems. An ecosystem contains one or more habitats. A **habitat** is the place where a living organism (e.g. plant, animal or micro-organism) lives. A burrow in garden soil, for example, is an earthworm's habitat. The other main part of an ecosystem is the **community** which is made up of all of the plants, animals and micro-organisms living there.

The plants, animals and micro-organisms form populations. A **population** is a group of living organisms of the one type (e.g. a forest of silver birch trees, a herd of deer, a colony of bacteria, etc.).

Thus an ecosystem is a natural biological unit which is made up of a community of living things, their own living surroundings and the factors that affect the lives of all the members of the community.

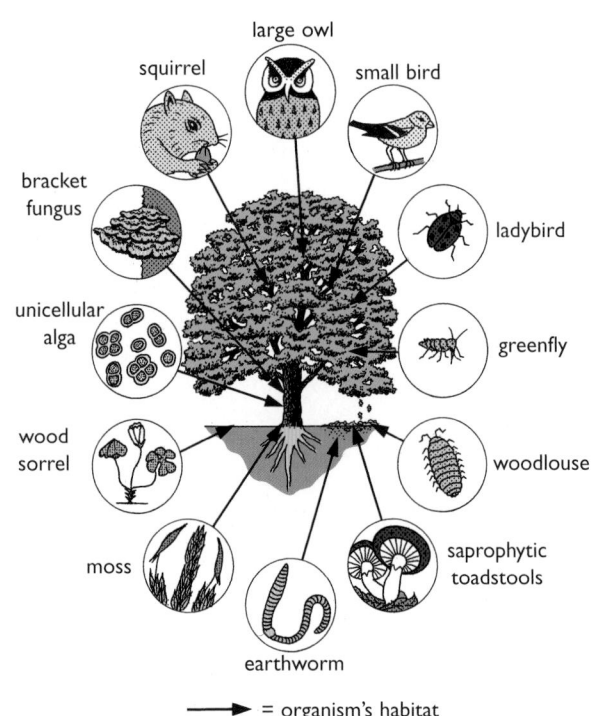

Figure 1.1 Oak tree ecosystem

Figure 1.2 Soil ecosystem

Biotic and abiotic factors

Factors related to living things such as amount of available food, number of predators, incidence of disease and competition for the necessities of life are called **biotic** factors.

Non living factors such as temperature, rainfall, light intensity and pH are called **abiotic** factors (also see page 9).